ENGLISH SHORT STORIES
FOR BEGINNERS

Learn English With Stories From an American Life

1st Edition

LANGUAGE GURU

ISBN: 978-1-950321-46-9

TABLE OF CONTENTS

INTRODUCTION

Wwe all know that immersion is the tried and true way to learn a foreign language. After all, it's how we got so good at our first language.

The problem is that it's extremely difficult to recreate the same circumstances when we learn a foreign language. We come to rely so much on our native language for everything, and it's hard to make enough time to learn a new one.

We aren't surrounded by the foreign language in our home countries. More often than not, our families can't speak this new language we want to learn. And many of us have stressful jobs or demanding classes that eat away at our limited energy and hours of the day. Immersion can seem like an impossibility.

What we can do, however, is gradually work our way up to immersion no matter where we are in life. And the way we can do this is through extensive reading and listening.

If you have ever taken a foreign language class, chances are you are familiar with intensive reading and listening. In intensive reading and listening, a small amount of text or a short audio recording is broken down line by line, and then, you are drilled on grammar endlessly.

Extensive reading and listening, on the other hand, is quite the opposite. You read a large number of pages or listen to hours and hours of the foreign language without worrying about understanding everything. You rely on context for meaning and try to limit the number of words you need to look up.

If you ask the most successful language learners, it's not intensive but extensive reading and listening that delivers the best results. Simply, volume is much more effective than explicit explanations and rote memorization.

To be able to read like this comfortably, you must practice reading in the foreign language for hours every single day. It takes a massive volume of text before your brain stops intensively reading and shifts into extensive reading.

This book hopes to provide a few short stories in English you can use to practice extensive reading. These stories were written and edited by native English speakers from the United States. We hope these short stories help build confidence in your overall reading comprehension skills and encourage you to read more native material. They offer supplementary reading practice with a heavy focus on teaching vocabulary words.

Vocabulary is the number one barrier to entry to extensive reading. Without an active vocabulary base of 10,000 words or more, you'll be stuck constantly looking up words in the dictionary, which will be sure to slow down your reading early on. To speed up the rate at which you read, building and maintaining a vast vocabulary range is absolutely vital.

This is why it's so important to invest as much time as possible into immersing yourself in native English every single day. This includes both reading and listening as well as being around native speakers through any and all means possible.

We hope you enjoy the book and find it useful in growing your English vocabulary and bringing you a few steps closer to extensive reading and fluency!

HOW TO USE THIS BOOK

(FOR STUDENTS)

H ello, I am the writer of the short stories. Before we get started, there are a few things I would like to say.

I promise I will try not to use too many words that are difficult. When there is a difficult word I have to use, I will write it like **this**. You can check what the word means in the "Vocabulary" part for that chapter.

Read through each chapter just once and no more. After reading, test yourself by answering the questions at the end. These questions will test how well you understood the story and vocabulary. You can find the answers to these questions at the back of the book.

It is recommended that you don't read the stories out loud. This will slow down your reading and learning. Being able to read fast will help you learn fast. If you want to practice speaking what you are learning, it is recommended to talk with a teacher instead.

If you want to review what you learned, making flashcards can really help. Programs like Anki or even the Goldlist method work great here. Make a few flashcards for the sentences you thought were hard. Use flashcards to test yourself to see if you can remember what these sentences mean. Try not to make too many, however. Studying and reviewing are important, but reading and listening are more important.

Reading helps us grow our vocabulary. Languages use thousands of words, and reading is the beginning to learning them all. Reading and understanding is the first step.

Listening is just as important too. I'm sure you have favorite TV shows or movies in English. The problem is that they can be hard to understand when you watch them in only English. I want to say you should try anyway. At first, you might be bored trying to watch something you don't understand. So pick something easy or something you have seen before. You'll have more fun and learn a lot too.

Make sure you read and listen to English as much as you can. Reading for just one or two hours a week isn't going to help very much. And it's the same for listening too. If you want to get really good at English, it has to be a big part of your life. Try to find new hobbies where you have to read or listen to something in English. For example, try listening to podcasts while going for long walks. You could also try video games.

And now, it is time to begin the stories. Let's get started.

CHAPTER ONE:

CHILDHOOD

Hi, my name is Jack. I want to tell you my story. It's a story about **figuring out** who you are. To tell this story, I will use 12 short stories. These stories happened at different points of my life. I hope you like them, and I hope they make learning English easier and more fun for you.

Let's start with childhood. Do you remember when you were a kid? I do, and I can't forget it. It was great. I remember eating ice cream on hot summer days with friends. We would chat while we ate and then go **hang out** at our friend Austin's house.

His house was the biggest in our **neighborhood**. It was **massive**. That house was the perfect place that had everything. The living room had big, soft sofas with a nice TV we watched our favorite cartoons on. The **basement** was large too. We used to play **hide-and-seek** and other games down there. And in the **yard**, which was also big, we ran around. Sometimes we **pretended** we had guns to shoot each other with.

My house wasn't as nice, but it was nice enough. A couple of times a week, my mom cooked dinner for me, my brothers, and my dad. **There's nothing like** your mom's cooking. It's some of the best food you'll ever eat. No **5-star** meal can compare to my mom's pasta.

Did your mom make you eat your vegetables? Mine did. **Green beans** and carrots were OK. But I could not eat **peas** at all as a kid. They were **nasty**.

One time at dinner, I hid them in my **mashed potatoes**. I made sure my parents weren't looking. And then, I picked up the potatoes and peas with my spoon. Finally, I **wiped** the spoon under the dining room table. Yeah, that was nasty too, but it worked. My mom stopped cooking peas after that. I never had to eat them as a kid, which is funny, because I love peas now.

I **got along** with my mom well but not my brothers. We **fought** all the time. My older brother was **mean** to me a lot. And a couple of our fights became **physical**. We never got hurt seriously, however, which is good.

My younger brother sometimes got more attention than me from our parents. So I used to **secretly** go into his room and break his toys. It's something I'm not **proud** of. No one's childhood is perfect and filled with only happy **memories**.

My dad worked very hard to **support** our family. By the time I woke up to get ready for school, he had already left to go to work. And when I came home from school, he would still be at his job. So I did not see him very much during the weekdays. But on Saturday morning, we watched hours of cartoons. And on Sundays, we watched football games all afternoon. My dad was a simple man who liked to watch TV.

He and my mom took us kids on a vacation each summer. One time, I remember we **rented** a small house in the mountains for a week. The house was a beautiful **log cabin** near a large lake. Also near the house was a **resort** area with lots of fun activities. There, we rode **go-carts**. We played at **arcades**. And we even went **jet-skiing**.

Perhaps my favorite childhood memory has to be winter. Playing in the snow was probably the most fun I have ever had. Snowball fights with friends were great. I also loved to build snow **forts** and snowmen.

But the best part was finding the perfect place to **slide**. I still remember the largest hill in our neighborhood. It took two minutes to walk up each time, but the 15-second **ride** down was amazing!

After playing all day in the snow, I would go inside to **warm up**. In front of the **fireplace**, I would sit and drink a nice cup of hot chocolate. Those were good times.

I think it's important to remember our childhood sometimes. It can help us in times when we are **extremely** sad. We should remember what it is like to be happy. That's because one day we will be happy again.

Vocabulary

- **childhood** --- the time in your life when you are a child

- **figure out** --- to understand

- **hang out** --- to spend time at a place or with people

- **neighborhood** --- an area of a town or city that people live in

- **massive** --- very large

- **basement** --- rooms in a building that are below ground level

- **hide-and-seek** --- a game where you hide and others try to find you

- **yard** *(house)* --- the area in front or behind a house

- **pretend** --- to do things in a way as if sth. were true when it isn't

- **there's nothing like** --- used to say you really enjoy something

- **5-star** --- the best you can get or go to

- **green bean** --- a type of long, green bean eaten as a vegetable

- **pea** --- a small, round, and green seed eaten as a vegetable

- **nasty** *(bad)* --- bad or not attractive at all

- **mashed potatoes** --- cooked potatoes that have been made very soft

- **wipe** *[verb]* --- to move sth. over sth. else to remove sth. dirty

- **get along** --- to like someone and be friendly with them

- **fight** *(argue)* --- to argue

- **mean** *(not kind)* --- not kind

- **physical** *(violent)* --- violent

- **secretly** --- in a way that is hidden from other people

- **proud** --- feeling happy about what somebody has or has done

- **memory** *(event)* --- something you remember

- **support** *(life)* --- to give sb. food, clothes, and a place to live

- **rent** *(pay)* --- to pay somebody money to use sth. they own

- **log cabin** --- a small house made from very thick pieces of wood

- **resort** *(place)* --- a place where many people go for a vacation

- **go-cart** --- a small, low car used for racing

- **arcade** *(games)* --- a place where you can play video games using coins

- **jet-skiing** --- riding across the water on a special machine

- **fort** --- a building or buildings used to protect against attacks

- **slide** *(move)* --- to (make sth.) move very easily over sth.

- **ride** *(journey)* --- a journey by car, bus, bike, train, or plane

- **warm up** *(temperature)* --- to (make something) become warmer

- **fireplace** --- a space in a wall in a room for a fire

- **extremely** --- a stronger word for "very"

Comprehension Questions

1. What did Jack say his story is about?
    A) Figuring out who you are
    B) Why winter is his favorite season
    C) His friend's house
    D) His family

2. Which of the following did Jack and his friends not do?
    A) Pretend to shoot each other with guns
    B) Play hide-and-seek
    C) Drink hot chocolate on cold winter nights
    D) Watch cartoons on TV

3. What happened when Jack fought with his older brother?
    A) They called each other names.
    B) Their fights sometimes became violent.
    C) They seriously got hurt.
    D) They were mean to their younger brother.

4. What did Jack and his dad watch on TV on the weekends?
    A) Cartoons and football games
    B) Nature and travel shows
    C) Cartoons and baseball games
    D) Cooking and game shows

5. What was not near the log cabin in the story?
    A) A resort area
    B) A large lake
    C) Mountains
    D) A small house

6. Which of the following is usually NOT made from snow?
    A) Snowballs
    B) Snow forts
    C) Snowmen
    D) Snow shoes

7. How did Jack warm up after playing outside in the cold?
    A) He sat behind the fireplace and drank hot chocolate.
    B) He sat in hot chocolate and drank it by the fireplace.
    C) He drank hot chocolate while sitting in the fireplace.
    D) He sat in front of the fireplace and drank hot chocolate.

CHAPTER TWO:

SCHOOL

Kids **tend** to really like or really hate school. I actually really liked school. It made me feel good about myself and like I could do something in the world.

Classes were easy in **elementary school**. Math, for example, was simple. Everyone can add and **subtract**, right? And most people can do long **division**, I think. I hope. It's really not that hard. I wasn't the **super** smart kid, and you don't have to be to do division. If you listened in class and followed instructions, anyone could do it, I thought.

Reading and writing were also no problem. Most of the time, two or three pages were all we had to read. And one paragraph was the most we were asked to write.

There were some longer **assignments** like book reports of course. And there were some difficult **topics** to understand in history and science. I remember the **Colonial Period** being long and boring. **Physics** was also hard for me to understand. Even now, I still don't know why the sky is blue. But I always tried and did my best which was enough.

Yet some kids had trouble **focusing** during class. I didn't understand why as a child. I thought the work was pretty easy. But now as an adult, I completely **get** it. It's really boring for them, and I feel bad for those kids who don't like school.

I also had my **struggles** in school too. Science and history were no problems for me, but I found it hard to **make friends**. Being the quiet kid didn't really help. I was afraid to **approach** other people and talk to them.

And when I did say something, it was usually **weird** or strange. I quickly learned that I was **awkward**. Being **naturally** awkward made it hard to even be around other people. But as a kid, this didn't worry me too much. I learned to like being alone.

Getting good **grades** was more important to me anyways. With good grades came **praise** from my teachers and parents. These conversations were the few times I felt good while talking with someone. Maybe they were just being nice to me. But either way, I liked the attention.

One day, I remember my parents told me I should be an **accountant**. I was good at math, so they thought this would be the best job for me. Today I laugh and smile when I think about the idea. I would have been a terrible accountant or **at least** a very unhappy one.

I liked math **for sure**, but I didn't know what I was really good at. How **is** a 10-year-old **supposed to** know what they are really good at? **In fact**, how is an 18 year old supposed to know that? Even at 30, I wasn't sure.

We are **pressured** to know these kinds of things early in life. And we have to make big decisions before we're actually ready. We may never even find out what kind of work matches us best. All we can do is to take a guess and hope we're right.

As a kid, there was no job that interested me. I didn't want to be a doctor, lawyer, teacher, or anything.

But I did have big dreams. I just didn't know what I would do. Yet I knew it would be something big. Maybe I would be an actor. Maybe I would be an **inventor**. Or maybe I would be an **astronaut**. All I knew was that I would definitely not be an accountant. I hate **taxes**.

Vocabulary

- **tend** *(be likely)* --- to be true usually

- **elementary school** --- a school for kids between ages 5-12

- **subtract** --- to take away one number from another number

- **division** *(math)* --- an example of division is (40 ÷ 8 = 5)

- **super** *[adverb]* --- *(informal)* very

- **assignment** *(work)* --- a piece of work someone is given to do

- **topic** --- a thing that people talk, write, or learn about

- **Colonial Period** *(America)* --- American history from 1607-1775

- **physics** --- the science of objects and energy

- **focus** *(give attention)* --- to do work on only one thing

- **get** *(understand)* --- to understand

- **struggle** *(effort)* --- something very difficult to do

- **make friends** --- to become friends with someone

- **approach** *(come near)* --- to come closer to something

- **weird** --- very strange

- **awkward** *(embarrassing)* --- making people feel embarrassed

- **naturally** *(born with)* --- in a way that somebody was born with

- **grade** *(score)* --- a letter or number to show how good sth. is

- **praise** *(approval)* --- words that show that you think sth. is good

- **accountant** --- sb. who keeps records of money received and paid

- **at least** *(less)* --- used to make sth. you just said less certain

- **for sure** --- *(informal)* definitely

- **be supposed to** --- to be expected to do something

- **in fact** --- used to give extra information about what you said

- **pressure** *[verb]* --- to try to make someone to do something

- **inventor** --- sb. who makes sth. that has never been made before

- **astronaut** --- somebody who travels and works in space

- **tax** --- money that you have to pay the government

Comprehension Questions

1. Why did Jack like school?
    A) It made him feel good about school.
    B) It made him feel good about himself.
    C) It made him feel good about the world.
    D) It made him feel good about other kids.

2. Which of the following are things you do in math?
    A) Addition, subtraction, and division
    B) History, science, and reading
    C) Accounting, taxes, and book reports
    D) Physics, Colonial Period, writing

3. How did Jack struggle in school?
    A) He wasn't good at history and science.
    B) He didn't understand the Colonial Period.
    C) He didn't get good grades.
    D) He had a hard time making friends.

4. What is another way to say the word "awkward"?
    A) Afraid of people
    B) Not liked by people
    C) Weird and strange
    D) Making people feel afraid

5. Why was Jack getting praise from his teachers and parents?
    A) He was very quiet and always listened in class.
    B) He was a good accountant.
    C) He was always laughing and smiling.
    D) He was getting good grades in school.

6. What does Jack say we are pressured to know early in life?
    A) What are the right decisions to make
    B) How to be good at math
    C) What kind of work we want to do
    D) What an accountant does

7. What kind of dreams did Jack have?
    A) Dreams of being an actor
    B) Dreams of being an inventor
    C) Dreams of being an astronaut
    D) Dreams of doing something big

CHAPTER THREE:

GAMES

I was naturally interested in video games while growing up. It's the perfect hobby for people who prefer being alone. I liked the idea of sitting in my room in **peace** playing a game. And if it was a great game, I could spend all day and night with it.

Video games are now a **billion**-dollar business. They say games make even more money than movies, music, and sports. Even if you don't play games, this fact is pretty **impressive**.

Let's take a quick **look** at what makes games so popular. Games offer all kinds of **experiences** and adventures. Some of which you can't have in real life. You can play as a **warrior** and fight against monsters from another world. Or you can play as a **wizard** and fight to save the Earth.

There are also **racing**, fighting, and shooting games too, of course. These are just some examples of the most popular gaming choices. There are also many more types of games out there, like **puzzle** games.

Many amazing moments can be had when you find a game that you really like. For example, it feels great when you finally beat a difficult **level** in a game. It's a very **rewarding** feeling. This is especially the case after hours, days, or even weeks of **failures**.

Finishing a game can make us feel we **accomplished** something big. Finishing building something large in a **crafting** game can give us the same feeling too. And how about when you win a really **close** match against another player? It is the best.

Games can also show us the power of our **imagination**. Playing a **horror game** can show us the scariest parts of our imagination. It can make us feel all kinds of **fear**. This is especially true when you don't know where the monster is. It's even scarier when you don't know what it looks like yet.

In other games, you have to use your imagination to **solve** a difficult problem. When the answer isn't **obvious**, you really need to think carefully. Finding the right **solution** can take time. But when you do find it, you will feel really smart and clever. It's a great feeling that a game can give you.

Some people say games can even be art. This is because they can make you feel things like a movie or painting does.

Not all games are art, of course. Sometimes people just want to play a **mindless** shooting game after a long day of work. And there's nothing wrong with that. It's no different than watching a mindless **action movie**.

There are, however, many **incredible** stories told through some games. But why not just read a book or watch a movie to find a good story? Why try to tell a story through a video game? The reason is because it offers a **unique** way to tell a story. Games are **interactive** while movies and books are not. If done well, an interactive story can give you an experience you've never had before. And it's beautiful.

Finally, there are games which are very **competitive**. They are like sports. Some people play and practice at these types of games for thousands of hours. As a result, they become very good at them.

And if the game is fun to watch, thousands or even millions of people will **tune in**. They will watch the best at the game play in large **events** for big cash prizes.

Competitive matches can be very exciting. And the action is easy to **follow**. You don't even have to have played the game being **broadcasted** before.

When I was younger, I played many of these kinds of games but now not so much. When we are young, there is often a need to **prove ourselves** by winning something. But when I got older, I realized there was **no longer** a need to win anything. The fun in games came from just playing them, not winning them.

Life works in the same way. I now see people playing the game of life in two different ways. There are people who try to win at everything. For example, there are people that try to make the most money as possible.

On the other hand, there are also people who try to have the most fun as possible. Winning is fun, but it also ends the game. And you don't always win when you play to win. Playing to have fun, however, keeps the fun going for **as long as possible**. And **in the end**, everyone always wins.

Vocabulary

- **peace** *(calm)* --- when it is calm and quiet

- **billion** --- 1,000,000,000

- **impressive** --- very good, important, or large

- **look** *(study)* --- studying a problem or situation carefully

- **experience** *(life)* --- something that happens to you

- **warrior** --- a person who fights or has fought in a battle or war

- **wizard** *(magic)* --- a person who can use magic

- **racing** --- any sport or game that involves races

- **puzzle** *(game)* --- a game you have to think carefully about to win

- **level** *(game)* --- one of the stages in a game

- **rewarding** *(feeling)* --- makes you happy after working hard

- **failure** *(has failed)* --- a person or thing that has failed

- **accomplish** --- to finish something with success

- **crafting** --- making something using your hands

- **close** *(competition)* --- won by only a small amount

- **imagination** *(power)* --- the power to create ideas in your mind

- **horror game** --- a scary game

- **fear** *(scared)* --- a strong feeling of being really scared

- **solve** --- to find a good or correct answer to a problem

- **obvious** --- easy to see or understand

- **solution** *(answer)* --- an answer to a problem

- **mindless** *(no thoughts)* --- not needing any thought

- **action movie** --- a film where lots of exciting things happen

- **incredible** --- very surprising, good, or large

- **unique** *(only one)* --- the only one like this

- **interactive** *(computer)* --- allows sb. to send information to sth.

- **competitive** *(want to win)* --- when sb. is trying very hard to win

- **tune in** --- to watch or listen to a program

- **event** *(planned)* --- a planned activity involving lots of people

- **follow** *(understand)* --- to understand

- **broadcast** *[verb]* --- to send out a program to watch and listen to

- **prove yourself** --- to show people that you are good at something

- **no longer** --- used when something was true but isn't true now

- **on the other hand** --- used to introduce sth. completely different

- **as long as possible** --- keep going until you can't

- **in the end** --- after considering everything

Comprehension Questions

1. According to Jack, which business makes the most money?
   A) Games
   B) Movies
   C) Music
   D) Sports

2. Which of the following would feel the most rewarding?
   A) Eating cake and ice cream
   B) Imagining your fears
   C) Failing again and again
   D) Solving a difficult puzzle

3. Which of the following is an example of using your imagination?
   A) Taking a shower
   B) Writing a story
   C) Making a cup of tea
   D) Reading instructions

4. Which of the following is the least mindless activity?
   A) Finding a solution to a difficult problem
   B) Sleeping in your bed
   C) Watching an action movie after work
   D) Watching paint dry

5. If something is competitive, it means that...
    A) people are not having fun.
    B) people are playing to have fun.
    C) people are playing to win.
    D) people are not winning.

6. What kind of things can people tune into?
    A) Puzzles and adventures
    B) Computers and games
    C) TV and radio shows
    D) Movies and work

7. According to Jack, how is life like a game?
    A) You can play to win or to have fun.
    B) You can make as much money as possible.
    C) You can prove yourself by winning.
    D) You can play as long as possible.

CHAPTER FOUR:

SPORTS

Sports are a very big part of some people's lives. It has no part in others' lives at all. For me, I used to hate sports. It used to be something I had to do **rather than** something I wanted to do.

My dad made my brothers and I play both football and baseball starting at six years old. The games **themselves** were fun to play. Throwing, catching, and kicking the ball was simple, good fun. But there was one problem. I was the **wimpy** kid.

During practice, our **coaches** worked us hard. They **trained** us with a lot of difficult exercises. They needed their players to be **tough** so that they played at their best.

But I didn't want to be tough. I didn't want to **roll** around in a field and get dirty. And I didn't want to **sweat**. Most **importantly**, I really hated running as a kid. That was the worst part.

Maybe I was **out of shape**. Maybe I was a little fat. But I just did not care at all.

And after I got hit by a baseball while **at bat** one day, I was done. I quit both football and baseball at the age of 12.

There was an **opportunity** to try other sports, but I had no interest at all. Soccer, **lacrosse**, and basketball were all pretty popular with kids my age. But it didn't matter to me. And forget about **cross-country**. I hated running, so why would I want to run in a race?

For me, **middle school** was all about video games. The perfect day was when I didn't have to do anything or go anywhere. On those days, I could wake up and play games all day long until it was time for bed. And I ate delicious **junk food** while I had a great time with some amazing games.

But as I got older, my body grew **weaker**. And I had gotten fat from all the junk I ate. My days were spent sitting at a computer desk 12 to 16 hours a day. It was not a healthy **lifestyle**. I also **rarely** ever saw the sun.

One day in high school, I came home from school and lied in my bed. I had been feeling sad and **lonely** for quite some time. It was then I **suddenly** realized I did not like myself. I have really bad memories from that day. But the next day, I made a decision. It was time for a change.

Ever since that day, I started going for a **jog** every day. That's right. I actually started running.

I remember being **out of breath** just after 30 seconds on the first day. If I was out of shape before, now I was really out of shape. But I kept going. I wanted to change myself **desperately**. I would do anything to change.

And with every month that passed, I got better. My **weight** was going down. And my **stamina** was going up. It felt great to watch myself grow and make **progress**.

From there, I learned that I really liked **biking** and other exercise too. Any exercise I could listen to music while **working out** was fun to me. **Techno** music was a big help in getting me back to good health. For this reason, I didn't like swimming. **Weightlifting**, however, was a great time.

To this day, exercise is a part of my daily **routine**. It has saved my life. It's that important. So I always make sure to do something **physical** every day. Some days I just go for a long walk, and each time I feel so much better after.

I love weightlifting, biking, and even running, but I am no **athlete**. I do have great **respect** for athletes, however. The hard work they do is incredible and impressive. When we watch sports on TV, we're watching the results of that hard work. And when I see a great **play**, it makes me think sports can be art too.

Vocabulary

• **rather than** --- instead of

• **themselves** *(focus)* --- used to focus on the subject of the sentence

• **wimpy** --- not strong

• **coach** *(person)* --- a person who helps people improve at sth.

• **train** *(prepare)* --- to (help sb.) prepare for a job or sport

• **tough** *(strong)* --- strong

• **roll** *(turn over)* --- to (make something) turn over and over

• **sweat** *(pass water)* --- to pass water in the body through the skin

• **importantly** --- used to say something is important

- **out of shape** *(person)* --- not in good condition *(of the body)*

- **at bat** --- trying to hit the ball in a baseball game

- **opportunity** --- a time when something can happen

- **lacrosse** --- a game played with a ball and long sticks with nets

- **cross-country** *(sport)* --- the sport of racing anywhere but roads

- **middle school** *(US)* --- a school for children from ages 10 to 14

- **junk food** --- food that is bad for your health

- **weak** *(not strong)* --- not strong

- **lifestyle** --- a way of living

- **rarely** --- not very often

- **lonely** *(sad)* --- unhappy because you have no one to talk with

- **suddenly** --- quickly and as a surprise

- **jog** *[noun]* --- a run you do at a slow speed for exercise

- **out of breath** --- having trouble breathing after exercise

- **desperately** *(very much)* --- very much

- **weight** *(being heavy)* --- how heavy something is

- **stamina** --- the power to do something difficult for a long time

- **progress** *[noun]* --- when something is improving

- **biking** --- riding a bicycle or motorcycle

- **work out** *(exercise)* --- to exercise

- **techno** --- fast dance music made with computers

- **weightlifting** --- picking up heavy things as a sport or exercise

- **routine** *(usual)* --- the usual way you do things

- **physical** *(body)* --- involving the body

- **athlete** --- someone who is very good at sports and exercise

- **respect** *(feeling)* --- a strong feeling that someone is very good

- **play** *(game)* --- an action in a game

Comprehension Questions

1. Why did Jack hate sports as a kid?
    A) He was not a wimp.
    B) He didn't like practice.
    C) He was tough.
    D) He didn't like the games.

2. Which of the following did Jack not do during practice as a kid?
    A) Running
    B) Sweating
    C) Rolling around in a field
    D) Weightlifting

3. Which of the following is NOT a sport?
    A) Basketball
    B) At bat
    C) Lacrosse
    D) Weightlifting

4. Which of the following is part of a healthy lifestyle?
    A) Sitting at a computer all day
    B) Eating junk food
    C) Being sad and lonely
    D) Working out

5. If you are out of shape, it means that...
    A) your stamina is very low.
    B) you have trouble breathing.
    C) you cannot breathe.
    D) you need to listen to some techno music.

6. If you are doing something physical, then you are...
    A) fighting.
    B) not using your mind.
    C) using your body.
    D) working out.

7. Why does Jack have great respect for athletes?
    A) They are not wimpy.
    B) They work very hard.
    C) They do weightlifting, running, and biking.
    D) They play to have fun.

CHAPTER FIVE:

COLLEGE

For a young adult, college is **freedom**. It's the freedom to do **whatever** it is you want. There's no parents or teachers telling you what to do. And you are **surrounded** by people with the same new freedom. It's a very unique place to be.

College is still school of course but one that is quite large. You can study thousands of more subjects than you could in high school. For example, **robotics** is something high schools don't usually teach. But in university, you can take robotics classes or even ones for game **programming**.

That was what I **originally** studied during my first year, but there was a problem. Playing video games is one thing, but creating them is another. **Simply**, I did not like programming. It's a very unique and interesting kind of work, but it **wasn't for me**. And since I had no interest in art or music, I couldn't make any part of a video game.

Lucky for me, American universities allow you to change your **major** very easily. One day you could be training to be a **chemist**.

And the next day you're in **engineering**. What an amazing thing that is.

I hear universities outside America don't allow for this. But I think they should. I can't **imagine** my life if I had to stay in a job I didn't like.

History was where I chose to go next. I really liked history in high school, so I was hoping I would like it in college too. And I was right.

To study history, you need to do a lot of reading. And I mean a lot of reading. I wasn't going to be able to do all this reading while at home. I was always **distracted** while at home. Having the computer or TV very close by was too much. So I decided to do my reading at the **campus** library.

That library was incredible. I loved it and must have spent over a thousand hours in that place. It helped me focus for long hours. And it gave me many simple things to do on my breaks.

I would read for about 15-20 minutes then watch the people standing in line at the library cafe. It does sound boring, but for some reason, it relaxed me. Just seeing what people wore and hearing what drinks they ordered was enough. I even made it into a game where I tried to guess what they would order. It was a **silly** game, but we all make our own fun.

Because I spent most of my time at the library, I didn't go to very many college parties. There were a few I went to, yet I never felt 100% comfortable at one. I felt that I always had to **entertain** people at parties. I did learn how to **socialize**, but none of it was natural to me. In the end, I did make a few friends, so I must have done something right.

And of course, there was a lot of **alcohol** at each party. The first time I **tasted** beer it was awful. It tasted like **pee**. Quickly, however, you learn why so many people drink it. It's a very **addictive** drug.

And it's easy to have a bad time with it. **Throwing up** after drinking too much is not fun. And **hangovers** are the worst.

Besides parties, I did go to a few clubs and events on campus. And I **got to** meet all kinds of people from all across the world. I met people from Puerto Rico, Mexico, Russia, South Korea, and England. My conversations were always awkward, of course. But it was good to **connect** with people from different parts of the world.

At every **corner** on campus, there were new experiences you could have. I wish I did more, but I felt the most comfortable alone just reading and writing. This way I can say I have no **regrets**.

Well, there was one regret. Getting a **degree** in history wasn't the smartest of ideas. It didn't do much to help me build a **career** after college.

Vocabulary

- **freedom** *(power)* --- the power to do whatever you want

- **whatever** *(anything)* --- anything or everything

- **surround** --- to be everywhere around something

- **robotics** --- the science of making robots

- **programming** *(computer)* --- writing computer programs

- **originally** --- in the beginning

- **simply** *(easy)* --- in a way that is easy to understand

- **be for someone** --- to like or enjoy something

- **major** *(college)* --- the main subject people study in college

- **chemist** *(science)* --- a scientist who works with chemistry

- **engineering** --- the study of building machines, buildings, etc.

- **imagine** *(picture)* --- to make a picture in your head about sth.

- **distracted** --- can't pay attention to something

- **campus** --- the buildings and land inside a college

- **silly** *(embarrassing)* --- embarrassing

- **entertain** *(interest)* --- to keep someone interested

- **socialize** *(spend time)* --- to spend time with other people for fun

- **alcohol** *(drink)* --- beer, wine, etc.

- **taste** *(test)* --- to eat or drink something as a test

- **pee** *[noun]* --- yellow water you pass when you use the bathroom

- **addictive** --- hard to stop using or doing

- **throw up** --- to bring sth. from your stomach out of your mouth

- **hangover** --- being sick the day after drinking too much alcohol

- **besides** --- other than, also

- **get to do something** --- to have the chance to do something

- **connect** *(relationship)* --- to have a good relationship with sb.

- **corner** *(area)* --- an area of a place

- **regret** *[noun]* --- a sad feeling about a mistake you made

• **degree** *(school)* --- a record saying you completed a school course

• **career** *[noun]* --- the job or jobs you do during your working life

Comprehension Questions

1. When you have freedom, you can...
    A) go to college.
    B) be in a unique place.
    C) surround yourself with other people.
    D) do whatever you want to do.

2. If you don't like or enjoy something, you can say that...
    A) it's not your major.
    B) it's not for you.
    C) you can't imagine it.
    D) it's silly.

3. Why couldn't Jack read at home?
    A) He was distracted by his computer and TV.
    B) He was a slow reader.
    C) He liked being on campus.
    D) He needed coffee to read.

4. What does "we all make our own fun" mean?

    A) We all find our own ways to have fun.

    B) We all go to the library to have fun studying.

    C) We all have fun standing in line to order drinks at a cafe.

    D) We all watch people and make it a fun game.

5. Which of the following is a way you can socialize?

    A) Talking with people

    B) Hanging out with people

    C) Going out with people

    D) All of the above

6. According to Jack, why do people drink alcohol?

    A) It tastes awful.

    B) It's a very addictive drug.

    C) It makes you pee.

    D) There's a lot of it at each party.

7. What was Jack's regret about college?

    A) He wished he was smarter.

    B) He wished he did more during college.

    C) His degree was not good for starting a career.

    D) None of the above

CHAPTER SIX:

JOBS

———

There is this **expression**. If you do what you love, you will never work a day in your life. This means that if you have a job that you love, it will never feel like work. I think this idea is very true, so I **applied** it to my time in college. The result was that I got a **useless** degree in history and lots of jobs I really did not like. I was also $40,000 in **debt**.

There are not many jobs that **require** a history degree. The only good you can do with it is to teach. This was the original plan, but by my final year, I had lost all interest. Even the idea of working in a museum didn't sound fun at all. **The truth** was that I didn't care for history at all anymore.

In my time at university, I got to do real history work. And writing **papers** is the main part of the job.

To write them, you need to read a lot of books. You will often have to go get a book and read about 30 pages of it. Only then you'll realize it's completely useless to your **research**. This **process** repeats many times before you finish a single paper. It's boring work that makes you feel like you're **wasting** your time.

So that is how I **ended up** working at a fast-food restaurant. I still lived at home, and I had to use my dad's car to get to and from work. These were not good times. I was very **depressed**.

I **showed up** late to work every day by 30 minutes. Many times I slept in the break room when I should have been working. And when I was working, I did my job very **poorly**. I'm sure I almost **caused** the business to fail. One day, I forgot that I was **scheduled** to come in for work, so I never showed up. The next day, I was **fired**. It was not my proudest day.

From there, I worked as a waiter at an Italian restaurant. I was feeling a little bit better at the time, so I actually **tried my best** here. But there was a problem. I **wasn't cut out** to be a waiter. You need to be quick and remember many **requests** from customers while moving fast.

Since I couldn't do this very well, I became a **busboy** a few weeks later. The job was so much easier. The pay, however, was awful. And after a few months, I quit.

My next job was at a **retail** store. A very large **corporation** owned this store and thousands of other stores across the world. During my time here, I worked as a **cashier**. And it **drove me crazy**. You have to stand in one place for many hours at a time and do the same things **over and over**. That's usually what you do at any job, but this one felt like **torture**.

I will always remember that feeling and also the break room. That room had the most unhappy people I've ever seen. They were just sitting down at the table, but you could tell something was wrong with them. There was no hope in their eyes. They looked like they had seen **hell**.

If I stayed at this job long enough, I was sure the same would happen to me. So I left.

I did several interviews for jobs that offered good careers and great pay, but they never went well. I remember this one interview for a sales **position**. I didn't know a single thing about selling, yet I tried anyways. I was hoping my college degree would get me the job, but the **interviewer** didn't seem to care. No **employer** seemed to care either. I had no real job **experience**, so I was useless to these companies. And that made me feel useless to the world.

My life was **going nowhere**. I was going to be **stuck** living with my parents. I was going to be poor and in debt **forever**. And I was scared that things were never going to get better.

I was depressed, but I wasn't ready to quit. So it was time for a new plan.

Vocabulary

- **expression** *(words)* --- a word or group of words

- **apply** *(use)* --- to use something

- **useless** *(not useful)* --- not useful

- **debt** *(money)* --- money that someone has to pay someone else

- **require** *(be necessary)* --- to need

- **the truth** --- the true facts about something

- **paper** *(study)* --- a piece of writing done after studying a subject

- **research** *[noun]* --- careful study of a subject to find new facts

- **process** *(doing)* --- a set of things you do to get a result

- **waste** *(not use well)* --- to not use something well

- **end up** --- to reach a place or situation after a long time

- **depressed** *(sad)* --- very sad for a long time

- **show up** *(arrive)* --- *(informal)* to come to a planned activity

- **poorly** --- in a way that is not good enough

- **cause** *[verb]* --- to make something happen

- **schedule** *[verb]* --- to plan sth. that will happen at a planned time

- **fire** *(from a job)* --- to make somebody leave their job

- **try your best** --- to do as much as you can

- **not be cut out** --- to not be the right person for something

- **request** *[noun]* --- asking for something

- **busboy** --- a person who takes away dirty dishes in a restaurant

- **retail** --- selling things to people in a store

- **corporation** --- a very large company or group of companies

- **cashier** --- a person whose job is to receive and give money

- **drive someone crazy** --- *(informal)* to make sb. angry or worried

- **over and over** --- repeating many times

- **torture** *(experience)* --- *(informal)* an awful experience

- **hell** *(experience)* --- a very awful experience

- **position** *(job)* --- a job

- **interviewer** --- the person who asks the questions in an interview

- **employer** --- a person or company that pays people to work

- **experience** *(skill)* --- skill you get from doing things

- **go nowhere** --- to not grow or change into something new

- **stuck** *(situation)* --- in a difficult situation that you can't change

- **forever** *(all time)* --- for all time

Comprehension Questions

1. If you are in debt, it means that...
    A) someone owes you money.
    B) someone has a lot of your money.
    C) you have no money.
    D) you owe someone money.

2. Why did Jack not like history in college?
    A) His research was useless.
    B) He felt he was wasting his time.
    C) He wasn't good at writing papers.
    D) History has too many repeating processes.

3. If you show up late to work and do your job poorly, then...
    A) you will probably be fired.
    B) you will be depressed.
    C) you will cause the schedule to fail.
    D) All of the above

4. Why did Jack become a busboy?
   A) He didn't try his best as a waiter.
   B) He was a boy who liked buses.
   C) He wasn't cut out to be a waiter.
   D) He was slow and didn't like customers.

5. How did Jack feel about his job as a cashier?
   A) He didn't like the corporation he worked for.
   B) He liked standing in one place for many hours.
   C) It was easy doing the same thing over and over.
   D) It felt like torture to him.

6. If someone has seen hell, it means that...
   A) they have watched fire destroy something.
   B) they have experienced something very horrible.
   C) they are very unhappy.
   D) they work as cashiers.

7. If you go to an interview for a position, it means that...
   A) you are an employer.
   B) you are trying to get a job.
   C) you have a good career that pays well.
   D) you have lots of job experience.

CHAPTER SEVEN:

OVERSEAS

It **turns out** that there was something I could do with my degree. I could travel the world and teach English. I first learned about the opportunity in college, yet I didn't **take it seriously**.

But now, this job was perfect for me. Many schools across the world were **hiring** and most only required a college degree. This was my chance to **move out** of my parents' home and even travel to a new country. There I could experience a different **culture** and learn a new language. It sounded like a real adventure.

And I loved the idea of teaching. While I no longer enjoyed history, this was not true for teaching. Working with kids was something I loved to do. And I had experience from a **tutoring** job in college.

There were many countries where you could teach English, but I chose South Korea. I had a few friends from there I had met at university. They were cool people born in a different culture with a different language. I wanted to learn more about their country. And I always **wondered** what they were saying in Korean during their conversations. The language was like a **mystery** to me, and I had to solve it.

After **applying** to a few schools and doing only two interviews, I had a teaching job. Did I get lucky? Or were they **desperate** for new teachers? I wasn't sure, but I was very excited just to have the job. Things were going well for me finally.

Applying for and getting my passport and **visa** took quite a long time. But once I had my **documents**, I was ready to go. It was time to fly.

My employer **purchased** my airplane ticket, and I packed my bags. I **boarded** the plane in Washington, D.C., and we took off for Seoul. Yet it would be a long while until we got there. We would be on that plane for quite some time.

The ride there was 14 hours long. You can only watch so many movies and shows before you get bored. And **good luck** trying to sleep in that small seat. It will make you really wish you had one of those beds in **first class**. Just for once in my life, I would like to fly first class.

We finally arrived at our **destination**. During the long taxi ride to my new apartment, I was **constantly** looking out of the windows. Everything was new around me. I had studied a little Korean before this point, so I **recognized** some of the writing on buildings. I saw **pharmacies**, banks, and schools, yet everything else was completely foreign to me. It was a big **culture shock**. For the first time in a long time, I was excited.

After arriving, my boss **greeted** me, and we chatted for a few minutes. He then **showed me around** my new apartment. After he left, the apartment was all mine. I was finally **free** again after living with my parents for so long after college. But just a minute later, I felt very sad. I was all alone, thousands of miles away from friends and family. I **couldn't help but** cry myself to sleep.

But I did sleep well that night. I needed it. I was going to need the **energy** for tomorrow. There was going to be a lot to **take in** for the next couple of days, weeks, and months. There would be many new **challenges** to come. There would be hundreds of opportunities as well. And going back to my job as a cashier was not going to be one of them.

Vocabulary

- **overseas** --- across the sea in, from, or to another country

- **turn out** *(be discovered)* --- to be discovered to be

- **take something seriously** --- to think something is important

- **hire** --- to pay someone to do a job

- **move out** --- to stop living in your old house

- **culture** *(way of life)* --- the way of life for a group of people

- **tutor** *[verb]* --- to teach someone outside of school

- **wonder** *(think)* --- to think about sth. and ask yourself questions

- **mystery** *(not known)* --- something that is not known

- **apply** *(job)* --- to ask for something in writing

- **desperate** *(wanting)* --- wanting or needing sth. very much

- **visa** --- a mark in your passport that allows you to enter a country

- **document** --- written information put on paper or a computer

- **purchase** *[verb]* --- to buy

- **board** *(get on)* --- to get on a plane, train, bus, or ship

- **good luck** --- used to say you hope someone gets sth. they want

- **first class** *(seat)* --- the most expensive seat on a plane, train, etc.

- **destination** --- a place someone is going to or sth. is being sent

- **constantly** --- all the time

- **recognize** --- to know what something is when you see or hear it

- **pharmacy** --- a store that sells medicine

- **culture shock** --- when you feel confused while in a foreign place

- **greet** --- to say hello or welcome someone

- **show sb. around** --- to be a guide for sb. who is new to a place

- **free** *(not controlled)* --- not under the control of someone or sth.

- **can't help but do something** --- to not be able to stop something

- **energy** --- power needed to do things

- **take in** *(understand)* --- to completely understand

- **challenge** *(test)* --- something difficult that tests your skills

Comprehension Questions

1. If you take something seriously, it means that...
    A) you think it's a funny joke.
    B) you think it's serious.
    C) it turns out to be serious.
    D) it's actually serious.

2. Why did teaching English seem to be the perfect job for Jack?
    A) It was a chance to move out of his parents' house.
    B) He could learn about a new culture and language.
    C) He had tutoring experience.
    D) All of the above

3. Which documents was Jack talking about in the story?
    A) College degree and ticket
    B) Application and interview
    C) Passport and visa
    D) Lucky and desperate

4. A first-class hotel room is usually what kind of room?
    A) A simple room with just a bed and TV
    B) A small and cheap room
    C) A very large and expensive room
    D) None of the above

5. How did Jack experience culture shock?

   A) He got lost during the taxi ride.

   B) He cried himself to sleep.

   C) He was free once again.

   D) Everything was new around him.

6. If your friend says he wants to show you around an area, ...

   A) he means he wants to guide you around the area.

   B) he means he wants to guide you around your new place.

   C) he means he wants to bring you to his apartment.

   D) he means he wants to bring you to your apartment.

7. What did Jack mean by "there was going to be a lot to take in"?

   A) There was a lot he had to eat.

   B) There was a lot he had to learn.

   C) There was a lot he had to finish.

   D) There was a lot of sleeping he had to do.

CHAPTER EIGHT:

TEACHING

The next day, I started my teaching job, and it turned out to be a lot of fun. I was a teacher for both elementary and middle school students.

My first classes each day were with elementary school kids. They had so much energy and said funny things that adults never would. Sometimes they told me the truth that adults were afraid to say. For example, I found out from a kid that my **breath** smells bad after drinking my morning coffee.

There were other moments of **shock** and surprise. I remember one day a student raised his hand in class. When I **called on** him, he said something so awful I don't even want to write it here. Just know that it had a **swear word** in it.

I was pretty upset after the student said this, so I immediately **punished** him for it. I made him stand in the back of the classroom with his arms **stretched** over his head. He had to stand there for 15 minutes before he could sit down. This was a **common** way to punish students at my school.

If this was an American school, things would be done **differently**. In America, this student would be sent to the **principal's** office. But this was Korea.

In Korea, if a student was taken out of class, it looked really bad for the school. The schools that I worked for were **private** businesses. Parents paid a lot of money each month to get a good English **education** for their kids. If their kids missed any of their class time, the parents and child changed schools. **Competition** between private schools was very high.

As a result, teachers in Korea have a lot of **responsibilities**. It was our job to both teach and **discipline** students.

This was different from the American school system. There, parents are more **responsible** for how their children act in school. If the child **misbehaves**, it's the parents who do most of the disciplining.

But in Korea, they do things differently, very differently. One day I left the classroom to go to the teachers' office. While I was walking down the hall, I saw our **head** teacher with a student. The student **lifted** one leg of his pants. His **calf** could now be seen.

The head teacher looked at me and said, "Sorry you have to see this." The teacher then hit the student's calf with his **pointer stick**. He **struck** him several times. And then, the student **limped** back into class followed by the teacher.

That was a true culture shock moment for me. Of course, I thought it was horrible for a teacher to hit a student. But this wasn't America. I was in a different place with different rules. What I thought didn't matter here.

The job had other **unpleasant** parts to it. Elementary school students had lots of energy and loved to talk, but this didn't last. When students started middle school, they got real quiet real fast. They became very serious. No one asked questions anymore, and no one **smiled** ever. Everyone also got worse at English. It happened to so many classes, and each time was just as sad.

I would also like to say my **lack** of training as a teacher made things harder. I did take a year of classes in college about teaching English, but those classes just taught **theories**. Teachers need **practical** training, however. They need simple **techniques** to help students learn. Knowing a subject is not enough to be able to teach it well.

I put a lot of **effort** into my first few years of teaching, but I didn't know what I was doing. Some progress was made with students, but it was **limited**. Only after I had received training years later, **real** progress started happening.

In the end, however, I couldn't see myself teaching English for the next 10 years. There's a few reasons why. First, as with many teaching jobs, I couldn't teach what I wanted. I had to teach what the school wanted.

Second, it was sad watching students' English get worse as they get older. They started to have more responsibilities, so they had fewer English classes per week. As a result, they seemed to slowly forget what they have learned over time.

And finally, teaching started to feel like a normal job. It no longer **excited** me like it used to.

I would have to find a new career **eventually**. But there was no need to hurry. I liked my job, and I had a whole country to **explore**.

Vocabulary

- **breath** *(the air)* --- the air that goes into and out of your body

- **shock** *(surprise)* --- a strong feeling of surprise

- **call on** --- to ask someone to speak or do something

- **swear word** --- a word used to be rude or with friends

- **punish** --- to cause pain to someone who has done sth. wrong

- **stretch** *(body)* --- to pull parts of the body

- **common** *(usual)* --- happening often

- **differently** --- in a way that is different

- **principal** *(school)* --- the person who has control of the school

- **private** *(business)* --- owned by a person and not the government

- **education** --- teaching and learning

- **competition** *(situation)* --- a situation where people are trying to win

- **responsibility** *(job)* --- something that is your job to deal with

- **discipline** *[verb]* --- to punish or teach sb. to act a certain way

- **responsible** *(job)* --- having the job of dealing with something

- **misbehave** --- to behave in a bad way

- **head** *(group)* --- the person who leads a group

- **lift** *(move)* --- to move something to a higher level

- **calf** *(leg)* --- the back of the lower part of your leg

- **pointer stick** --- a thing you use to point at something

- **strike** *(hit)* --- to hit something hard

- **limp** --- to walk slowly because one leg is hurt

- **unpleasant** --- not fun, attractive, or friendly

- **smile** *[verb]* --- to move your mouth up when you are happy

- **lack** *[noun]* --- not having something or enough of something

- **theory** *(idea)* --- one or more ideas that try to explain something

- **practical** *(real)* --- connected to real situations and not ideas

- **technique** --- a special way of doing something

- **effort** *(energy)* --- the energy you need to do something

- **limited** *(not very great)* --- not very great (in amount)

- **real** *(for emphasis)* --- used to show that something is important

- **excite** *(make happy)* --- to make sb. feel very happy and interested

- **eventually** --- at the end of a period of time

- **explore** *(travel)* --- to travel around a new area or country

Comprehension Questions

1. How did Jack punish the student in the story?
    A) He gave the student extra homework.
    B) He made him stand in the back of the classroom.
    C) He hit the student on the calf.
    D) He made him do a quick arm stretch.

2. What is another word for "punish"?
    A) Responsibility
    B) Competition
    C) Discipline
    D) Principal

3. Which of the following is NOT part of the lower human body?
    A) Feet
    B) Legs
    C) Arms
    D) Calves

4. Why was the student in the story limping back to class?
    A) He was struck on the leg many times.
    B) He hit the teacher on one of his calves.
    C) Jack hit the student's arms.
    D) The story does not say why.

5. What was Jack's problem with his classes on teaching English?
   A) They taught theories that were wrong.
   B) They taught techniques that were not helpful.
   C) They taught theories that were not practical.
   D) All of the above

6. What was Jack's problem with his job as an English teacher?
   A) He couldn't teach what he wanted.
   B) Students' English ability got worse as they got older.
   C) It stopped being exciting.
   D) All of the above

7. Why did Jack's students' English ability get worse over time?
   A) They became very serious.
   B) They stopped asking questions and even smiling.
   C) They had fewer English classes in middle school.
   D) They had to find a new career eventually.

CHAPTER NINE:

LANGUAGE

I quickly learned I would not get very far in Korea knowing just English. Almost no one spoke English outside of my school. Without Korean, I could not **communicate** with the people around me.

I had bought a **textbook** and begun studying before going to Korea. But progress had been slow. I only knew a few **basic** phrases before I got on the plane.

In an effort to learn vocabulary, I made many **flashcards**. They did help, but more was going to be needed, of course. I also put **sticky notes** around my home to help me learn new words. Did you do this as well? Many of us will do anything to learn.

I then started reading grammar textbooks. I also listened to **audio** lessons during my walks and bus rides. And after some practice, I could make my own sentences. People could now understand me, and basic communication became possible. It felt great. Maybe I could actually learn this language, I thought.

Then one day, an online advertisement for an event **caught my eye.** It was for a **language exchange** event. And it was happening that week at a cafe on a Sunday afternoon. I immediately **signed up** and was very excited about the idea. This would be a completely new experience for me.

Waiting those seven days felt like waiting a month. But finally, the day had arrived.

When I got to the cafe, I saw around 25 people that had already **gathered**. There were both Koreans and **foreigners** sitting at large tables talking in English and Korean. It was a beautiful **scene**.

My conversations, however, did not go as well as I hoped. **Tell me** if this has ever happened to you. You're talking to someone in English, and they say something you don't understand. The other person realizes this, and the conversation starts to slow down. They suddenly become bored talking with you, and you feel bad.

Or maybe this has happened as well. You start a conversation, and things are going good. After a few minutes, however, you don't know how to say something. But you find a way to **move on** and keep the conversation going. Then it happens a few more times, and you get **frustrated**. And you feel like a failure.

Both of these things happened to me at the event, but one good thing did come from it. I met another American, and he was very good at Korean. He spoke **fluently**. He could even make Koreans laugh at his jokes. I was pretty **jealous**, I have to say.

After the event was over, I walked up to him and asked for advice. "Don't worry about studying grammar and **memorizing** phrases. Try to learn **naturally**," he said. He told me to read and listen to **as much** Korean **as possible** every day. "Just try to understand what people are saying in stories and on TV shows. When you can do that, you'll be able to speak too."

And so I took his advice. I started to listen to Korean at every hour that I could. I watched a lot of Korean TV. My reading skills were pretty **poor**, but I read every Korean children's story I could. And then, I started reading the news and a lot of Korean comics.

Progress was very slow for the next six months. It didn't feel like I was getting any better. Almost every sentence I read or heard had words in it that I didn't know. And I was getting **tired of** looking up new words in the dictionary. It was frustrating.

But I didn't **give up**. I was a very **stubborn** person. If there ever is a challenge, I will do everything to beat it. And **within** one year, that challenge was beaten.

I was finally able to understand and enjoy what I was reading and listening to. The stories, shows, and movies were just amazing. To understand another country's culture and **media** is a great feeling. **So** is being able to speak a different language, I can now say.

There was just one question to answer now. What was I going to do with this new language I had learned?

Vocabulary

- **communicate** *(information)* --- to share information

- **textbook** --- a book with information on one subject

- **basic** *(simple)* --- simple or the starting point of something

- **flashcard** --- a card with a word or picture on it, used to teach

- **sticky note** --- a small piece of paper you can stick to something

- **audio** --- connected with recorded sound

- **catch someone's eye** --- to get someone's attention

- **language exchange** --- talking with sb. in two languages to practice

- **sign up** --- to sign a form agreeing to do something

- **gather** *(come together)* --- to come together to one place

- **foreigner** --- a person who comes from another country

- **scene** *(view)* --- a place, event, or situation that you can see

- **tell me** *(happen)* --- used when you think sth. happened to sb.

- **move on** *(to sth. new)* --- to start doing or discussing sth. new

- **frustrated** --- feeling angry because you can't do what you want

- **fluently** *(language)* --- speaking or reading a language well

- **jealous** *(want)* --- angry and unhappy because sb. has sth. you want

- **memorize** --- to learn something so you can remember it exactly

- **naturally** *(life)* --- happening as part of nature without any help

- **as much as possible** --- as much as you can

- **poor** *(bad)* --- not good

- **tired of something** --- bored of something

- **give up** *(stop)* --- to stop doing something before it's finished

- **stubborn** *(person)* --- very hard to change

- **within** *(time/area)* --- inside a period of time or an area

- **media** --- internet, newspapers, games, TV, books, movies, music ...

- **so** *(also)* --- also

Comprehension Questions

1. How much Korean did Jack know before going to South Korea?
   A) He knew nothing.
   B) He knew a few basic phrases.
   C) He could communicate on a basic level.
   D) He spoke fluently.

2. If you sign up to do something, it means that...
   A) you agree to sign a form.
   B) you will write a paper on something.
   C) you agree that you will do something in the future.
   D) you will sign something in the future.

3. What two problems did Jack have at the language exchange?
   A) He didn't have or make any friends.
   B) He was bored and frustrated.
   C) He couldn't understand people or say what he wanted.
   D) He felt stupid and like a failure.

4. If you are doing something as much as possible, then...
   A) you are doing as much of it as you want.
   B) you are making it possible to do.
   C) you are feeling it is possible to do.
   D) you are trying very hard to do it.

5. When you look up words in the dictionary, you are usually...
    A) trying to find what they mean.
    B) trying to memorize new words.
    C) trying to study grammar.
    D) All of the above

6. If you are stubborn, it means that...
    A) you don't stop changing.
    B) you don't give up.
    C) you feel great.
    D) you get frustrated.

7. Which of the following are examples of media?
    A) Culture and language
    B) Games and music
    C) Movies and papers
    D) Books and questions

CHAPTER TEN:

LOST

So there I was in Korea. I had been living there for three years by this point. But now I could speak Korean. Many more opportunities had become **open to** me because of that.

Through the language exchanges, I met a lot of people and made good friends. They invited me to many events, parties, and **get-togethers**.

I had a **blast** hanging out with Korean people. They were very friendly with me. Many were happy to go out with me and eat, drink, and sing karaoke.

Eating and drinking is a big part of Korean culture. You even have to often go out to eat and drink with your boss and **co-workers**. That was something I never did back home.

There were, however, Koreans that I did not connect with. Some people just weren't interested in spending time with an English teacher from a foreign country. These conversations made me feel my Korean wasn't good enough.

But **looking back** now, I see that wasn't important. Most people don't care about your language skill **as long as** you can communicate. They care about **whether** or not they enjoy hanging out with you. That's what's most important. You just need to keep looking until you find people that like you. Sure, language can and does make understanding difficult sometimes. But if the person likes you, they will try their best to communicate.

This is especially important in dating. Ever since I got to Korea, I really wanted to date a Korean girl. The idea was very exciting to me. And after meeting many Korean people, I had many chances.

One of these **encounters** became serious. We both really liked each other, and we spent a lot of time **getting to know** the other person. In our conversations, we spoke both Korean and English. It felt great to have a partner to help and get help from.

There were many dates we went on that I will never forget. One time, there was a **double date** we did. The girl I was dating had a friend who was also dating an American guy. And so we all went **bowling** and had drinks after.

During this double date, I chatted with the guy for quite a bit. He was in a bit of a **unique** situation. He was not an English teacher like most foreigners in the country. Instead, he worked as a computer programmer for a Korean company. So not only did he speak Korean, but he had a job skill as well.

I was very **impressed**, but he didn't seem proud of his work. To him, it was a normal job. He went to work, did his job, and went home. There was nothing special about it, he told me. In the end, he was another company **employee**, he thought.

He and his story really made me think. Was that the life I wanted? Of course not. There was no adventure in that kind of life. I wanted to live in Korea and learn Korean, but I didn't have any plan that came after.

I had accomplished that **goal**, so what now? I didn't want to teach English forever. And I didn't want to be a **translator** either.

There were no other job skills I had. And I didn't want to learn one. What was I doing here? Where was I going with this?

It was around this time that I stopped going out on the weekends. There were no more language exchanges for me. There was no more exploring the city. There was no more hanging out with friends. All I wanted to do was lie in bed and watch TV. And everything I watched was in English since Korean had no **value** to me anymore. For many months, this **went on**.

Many of us spend years **building** a life, and then suddenly, it means nothing to us. Has something like this ever happened to you? It's like a **long-term** relationship that comes to a very depressing end.

Speaking of relationships, there was only one reason I went out on the weekends. I was still dating that girl. I did my best to be happy around her. And we still did have amazing dates together.

One day, we finally became an **official** couple. We were boyfriend and girlfriend.

But something didn't feel right about it. I felt nothing when this moment happened. I felt **empty**. If I stayed with her, I was going to be very unhappy. If I stayed in Korea, I was going to be **miserable**.

And so I told her how I really felt. She was **incredibly** sad. She cried a lot. I wanted to cry, but I couldn't. Some people are taught by their parents to always hide their **emotions**. I was one of them.

The next month I quit my job and left the country. While it was a sad ending, I really loved my time there. I do not regret the years I spent there. It really was like an adventure. Those years taught me lessons I will never forget. Those experiences helped me become the person I am today.

Vocabulary

- **lost** *(situation)* --- not knowing what to do in a situation

- **open to sb.** --- when an opportunity is available to sb.

- **get-together** --- a relaxed and friendly meeting or party

- **blast** *(fun)* --- *(informal)* a very fun experience

- **co-worker** --- a person you work with at a company

- **look back** --- to think about something that happened

- **as long as** --- if

- **whether** --- if

- **encounter** *[noun]* --- a meeting that is not planned

- **get to know sb.** --- to spend time with sb. and learn about them

- **double date** --- when two couples go out on a date together

- **bowling** --- a game where you roll heavy balls at tall, white things

- **unique** *(special)* --- very special or unusual

- **impress** *[verb]* --- to make sb. think what you did or have is great

- **employee** --- someone who is paid to work for other people

- **goal** *(aim)* --- sth. you hope to finish or get after a lot of work

- **translator** --- a person who changes words into another language

- **value** *(useful)* --- something that has value is useful or important

- **go on** *(continue)* --- to continue

- **build** *(create)* --- to create or grow sth. over a long period of time

- **long-term** --- lasting for a long time

- **speaking of sth.** --- connected to the subject being discussed

- **official** *(public)* --- told to everyone

- **empty** *(feeling)* --- having no purpose or interest

- **miserable** *(unhappy)* --- always very unhappy

- **incredibly** *(extremely)* --- a stronger word for "very"

- **emotion** --- a strong feeling or feelings

Comprehension Questions

1. Why is this chapter called "Lost"?
    A) Jack got lost while traveling in Korea.
    B) Jack lost a game.
    C) Jack lost his job as a teacher.
    D) Jack felt lost while living in Korea.

2. A get-together is like which of the following?
    A) A party or event
    B) A meeting or vacation
    C) An event or showing
    D) A party or opportunity

3. How many people are involved in a double date?
    A) 2
    B) 4
    C) 6
    D) 8

4. Changing words from one language into another is called...
    A) translating.
    B) speaking.
    C) impressing.
    D) encountering.

5. What does the word "short-term" mean?
    A) Stopping for a short time
    B) Continuing for a short time
    C) Staying for a short time
    D) Lasting for a long time

6. Which of the following words can't be used to describe a feeling?
    A) Empty
    B) Sad
    C) Official
    D) Miserable

7. What did Jack regret about his time in Korea?
    A) He wished he chose a different country to live in.
    B) He wished he had a better job.
    C) He regretted everything.
    D) None of the above

CHAPTER ELEVEN:

ENTERTAINER

I was finally back home in America. I had returned to the home of the **bald eagle**, guns, and fast food. And to be honest, I had missed it. America does have some really cool things. Of course, it does have some problems too.

The one part I missed the most was our **entertainment**. We really do have some of the best in the world. American TV and movies can't be **beat**. We have great **literature**, music, and games too, but so do other parts of the world. American shows and films, however, are on **another level**.

I grew up watching amazing TV shows and movies but also with the internet. Maybe this was the same for some of you reading this as well. Do you remember life before and after the internet became popular? What a difference!

Before I left Korea, I did a lot of thinking about what I would do next. The idea of being an employee anywhere was not exciting to me at all. I wanted to be free to do what I wanted to do. Who doesn't want that?

For me, this meant I would have to start my own business. Being your own boss is true freedom. You **set** your own schedule.

And you decide what kind of work you will do. But unfortunately, for the first few years, you will be working all the time. And you will have to do whatever makes the most money just to stay in business.

I **was up to** the challenge. Once again, it felt like a real adventure. I was excited for the first time in a long time.

And I knew what kind of business I would do. I would become an entertainer. With social media, anyone can do it. All you need is an internet **connection**. You don't have to be an actor. You don't have to have any kind of training either. You just need to be entertaining in some way.

There's a lot of different types of **content** on social media. But I was interested in doing one kind **in particular**. I wanted to start my own show by recording and **posting** videos.

Like many shows on the internet, it didn't need to be **professional**. The entertainment comes from showing your **personality** on camera. The jokes are what make these videos so popular. Sometimes what is being discussed doesn't even matter. People come for the content but keep coming back for the personalities.

For my show, I started by **reviewing** books and posting my videos on all social media. I had found a **passion** for reading while in Korea. When I could no longer read and listen to Korean, I would read a little bit in English. There were incredible stories that **inspired** me. And I wanted to share them with the world.

My first few videos, however, were not very good. They were **flops**. Almost no one watched them. I did my best to **perform** on camera. I wrote **scripts**, practiced them, and spoke with passion. But the videos still did poorly. It was very **disappointing**.

So I decided that the next **set** of videos I did would be on video games. The topic of games was much more popular than books, and I had played a **bunch** of games growing up.

Immediately, these did much better. In fact, they were getting thousands of **views**. It was incredible.

Reading the **comments** was the best part. Most people were **positive** and very kind. To know you brought someone **joy** or even hope is an amazing feeling. That's the power of entertainment. It gave my work **meaning**.

And so I continued to make more videos. I also started learning video **editing** and using what I learned every day. People really liked the new **style** of videos. The numbers didn't **lie**. Some of these videos got more than 100,000 views. And they were making hundreds of dollars from ad **revenue**. I was in business.

And there was still so much more I could do to make better videos. I spent 12 hours a day editing using the new techniques I was learning. There are so many **effects** you can add to improve your work.

What you can make is beautiful, but the work can be extremely **stressful**. And that stress kept building and building with each new video. I always tried to do better than my last **project**.

It was kind of like what an artist does. They are always adding **details** until their art is perfect. Sometimes they can't do anything else until it's done. Sometimes they can't even eat or sleep because the work isn't finished.

Soon, I was working 16 to 18 hours a day on my videos. I was also working 30 days **straight** with no days off.

And then it happened. I had a **mental breakdown**. My hands wouldn't stop shaking. Then my whole body started shaking. I couldn't work, eat, sleep, or even drink water. I could only lie down in my bed and **suffer**. I thought I was going to die. This lasted for three days. It was one of the scariest experiences of my life.

After I **recovered**, I thought for a long time about the business I had built. All day I would **stare** at the floor in my room thinking about what had happened.

Finally, I decided it was best to quit it **altogether**. The stress of the job was going to kill me if I did not. No job was **worth** dying for.

And when I thought about it some more, I was making content that other people wanted. I wasn't making the content I wanted to make. Doing what was popular made me a lot of money, but it didn't make me happy. Even a child would know this would happen, so why didn't I?

I would need to do a lot more thinking. What did this all mean? Why did I care so much about that business? And where I would go next? With time, the answers would come.

Vocabulary

- **entertainer** --- someone who makes people enjoy themselves

- **bald eagle** --- a North American bird used as a symbol of the US

- **entertainment** --- shows, films, games, etc. made for you to enjoy

- **beat** *(do better)* --- *(informal)* to do or be better than something

- **literature** *(art)* --- written works seen as art

- **another level** --- to be much better than something else

- **set** *(decide)* --- to decide something

- **be up to something** --- *(informal)* to do something

- **connection** *(being connected)* --- being connected to something

- **content** *(internet)* --- information, pictures, or video on a website

- **in particular** --- especially

- **post** *(internet)* --- to put information, pictures, or videos online

- **professional** *(high level)* --- done at a very high level

- **personality** *(character)* --- the kind of person you are

- **review** *(opinion)* --- to give your opinion about a book, film, etc.

- **passion** --- a very strong feeling of liking or hating something

- **inspire** *(encourage)* --- to make sb. feel they want to and can do sth.

- **flop** *[noun]* --- sth. that isn't popular and makes little to no money

- **perform** *(entertain)* --- to entertain people by acting, singing, etc.

- **script** *(text)* --- the written words of a film, play, talk, etc.

- **disappointing** --- not as good as you hoped

- **set** *(group)* --- a group of things that belong together in some way

- **bunch** *(large)* --- a large amount or number of something

- **view** *(online)* --- the number of times something was seen online

- **comment** --- something you say or write that gives your opinion

- **positive** *(support)* --- showing support

- **joy** *(happiness)* --- a very strong feeling of being happy

- **meaning** *(purpose)* --- purpose

- **edit** *(change)* --- to make changes to some writing or a film

- **style** *(way)* --- a way something is done

- **lie** *(tell)* --- to say or write something that you know isn't true

- **revenue** --- the money a government or a business receives

- **effect** *(theater)* --- a light, sound, or object used in a play or film

- **stressful** --- makes you feel worried

- **project** *(work)* --- a piece of planned work done over a long time

- **detail** *(art)* --- a small part or all the smart parts of a piece of art

- **straight** *(following)* --- following one after another without stops

- **(mental) breakdown** --- a serious period of illness in the mind

- **suffer** *(feel pain)* --- to feel lots of pain in the mind and/or body

- **recover** *(health)* --- to become healthy again after an illness

- **stare** --- to look at someone or something for a long time

- **altogether** *(completely)* --- completely

- **worth** *(recommended)* --- used to recommend an action

Comprehension Questions

1. What did Jack miss most about his home country?
   A) The food
   B) The guns
   C) The entertainment
   D) The literature

2. According to Jack, what is most important in creating a show?
   A) How professional it is
   B) The personalities on camera
   C) What is being discussed
   D) The type of content

3. How did Jack bring people joy and hope?
   A) By reading their comments
   B) By being positive and kind
   C) By creating entertaining videos
   D) By giving his work meaning

4. What does Jack mean when he says "the numbers didn't lie"?
   A) Numbers can talk to people, and they don't tell lies.
   B) The views showed that people liked the new style of videos.
   C) The ad revenue said something that isn't true.
   D) All of the above

5. What was Jack doing to make better videos?
    A) Reading comments
    B) Earning lots of ad revenue
    C) Having a mental breakdown
    D) None of the above

6. Which word is another word for "pain"?
    A) Project
    B) Detail
    C) Straight
    D) Suffering

7. Which of the following helps you recover after getting sick?
    A) Food and sleep
    B) Mental breakdowns
    C) Stress and joy
    D) Bald eagles

CHAPTER TWELVE:

FINALE

For the next six months, my mornings were very quiet. I would wake up, make myself a cup of coffee, and just sit in my room. Most of this time I wasn't even thinking. Memories of my **past** came and went.

As a child, it was so easy to have fun. Joy was everywhere. But as an adult, I had lost it. Where had it gone?

Everything had **led** to this point. And there was joy at every step of the way. I liked school. I liked the games I got to play. I learned to like exercise and **appreciate** it and my health. I found a job I **truly** loved. I enjoyed my time overseas and the process of learning a new language. I even got the opportunity to build a **successful** business.

But who was I really? These were all just **phases** in my life. No single phase ever lasted for more than a few years. Nothing was **constant**.

Or maybe something was constant, and I just hadn't seen it. I must have stared at my bedroom floor for a thousand hours, but I was really looking inside myself for an answer. Maybe the answer would suddenly **appear**, I hoped. And then, one day, an idea came to me.

It was the writing I had enjoyed the most when **running** my business. There was something so **peaceful** sitting at my desk with just paper and pen. My head was always full of ideas, and I liked trying to put them into words. It was a joy to carefully pick the right words to **capture** an idea in a perfect way. That is where the joy of **creation** was.

Everything that came after the writing, however, was not fun. The filming, editing, and **managing** were nothing but stress. They were all **necessary** to making a good video, but I hated doing them.

The more I thought about my past, **the more** I saw a love for writing. I had studied and taught a foreign language, and writing is all about language. It's about using language to tell a story. I had studied history as well, and history, too, is all about telling a good story. It's a story about what happened in the past. Even the games I used to play told great stories in their own unique ways.

Reading had inspired me to write my own stories, but what would I write about? Usually writers write **novels**, but I never had any ideas about long stories with lots of characters. And besides, there are enough great novels out there already.

In fact, there are so many other ways to write a good story. And there are so many places that need them. For example, I remember the stories from my old Korean textbooks. They weren't very good. The stories were boring, and the language was too hard.

And then, it **hit** me. I could write better stories. I could tell more interesting stories than those **bland** ones. And I could make them easier for those learning new languages. That is the story of this book and several others I have made for language learners.

So that is where I am today. Writing is my job and passion. And when I'm not working, I enjoy long walks while listening to a good **audiobook**.

Wherever there is an opportunity to tell a great story, I will write it. I hope one day to write my own children's book. I also would like to do a **non-fiction** book as well. I may even do one on interesting people **throughout** history some day.

Maybe even one day I'll write that novel. And maybe one day you'll be a fluent **speaker** of English. Thanks for reading!

Vocabulary

- **finale** --- the last part of a show

- **past** *(life)* --- a person's past life or a place or group's history

- **lead** *(result)* --- to get something as a result

- **appreciate** *(understand)* --- to understand the good parts of sth.

- **truly** *(true)* --- used to say something is very true

- **successful** *(achieved)* --- getting the result you wanted

- **phase** *(step)* --- a step in the many changes sth. experiences

- **constant** *(happening)* --- happening all the time

- **appear** *(be seen)* --- to start to be seen

- **run** *(manage)* --- to do or be in control of

- **peaceful** *(quiet)* --- quiet and not worried at all

- **capture** *(describe)* --- to describe sth. very well using words or art

- **creation** *(creating)* --- creating sth. or the thing that is created

- **manage** *(control)* --- to control something

- **necessary** --- needed for something

- **the more...the more** --- used to say two things happen together

- **novel** *[noun]* --- a very long story with characters and events

- **hit** *(idea)* --- to come suddenly into your mind

- **bland** *(boring)* --- not interesting

- **audiobook** --- a recorded book that you listen to

- **wherever** --- in any place

- **non-fiction** --- writing that is about real things and people

- **throughout** *(during)* --- during the whole time of something

- **speaker** *(language)* --- sb. who speaks the language being discussed

Comprehension Questions

1. Jack did many things throughout his life but did NOT...
    A) play video games.
    B) go to college.
    C) write a novel.
    D) start a business.

2. If you run a business, what does that mean?
    A) You work for a business.
    B) You own a business.
    C) You start a business.
    D) All of the above

3. The more Jack thought about his past...
    A) the more he saw a love for writing.
    B) the more he hated his business.
    C) the more he wanted to learn about language.
    D) the more history books he wanted to read.

4. What is a novel?
    A) A very bland story with lots of events
    B) A very peaceful story with lots of characters
    C) A piece of non-fiction
    D) A very big story with lots of people and things that happen

5. If an idea hits you, it means that...
    A) you are very smart.
    B) you are ready to write a novel.
    C) you suddenly think of something.
    D) it's very bland and not interesting at all.

6. If someone says you can sit wherever you like, then...
    A) you can sit anywhere you would like.
    B) you can sit everywhere at the same time.
    C) you can sit nowhere at all.
    D) you can sit somewhere, but they are not sure where.

7. Which of the following is non-fiction?
    A) Science
    B) Business
    C) History
    D) All of the above

ABOUT THE AUTHOR

Language Guru is a brand created by a hardcore language enthusiast with a passion for creating simple but great products. They work with a large team of native speakers from across the world to make sure each product is the absolute best quality it can be.

Each product and new edition represents the opportunity to surpass themselves and previous works. The key to achieving this has always been to work from the perspective of the learner.

DID YOU ENJOY THE READ?

Thank you so much for taking the time to read our book! We hope you have enjoyed it and learned tons of vocabulary in the process.

If you would like to support our work, please consider writing a customer review on Amazon, Goodreads, or wherever you purchased our book. It would mean the world to us!

We read each and every single review posted, and we use all the feedback we receive to write even better books.

ANSWER KEY

Chapter 1:
1) A
2) C
3) B
4) A
5) D
6) D
7) D

Chapter 2:
1) B
2) A
3) D
4) C
5) D
6) C
7) D

Chapter 3:
1) A
2) D
3) B
4) A
5) C
6) C
7) A

Chapter 4:
1) B
2) D
3) B
4) D
5) A
6) C
7) B

Chapter 5:
1) D
2) B
3) A
4) A
5) D
6) B
7) C

Chapter 6:
1) D
2) B
3) A
4) C
5) D
6) B
7) B

Chapter 7:
1) B
2) D
3) C
4) C
5) D
6) A
7) B

Chapter 8:
1) B
2) C
3) C
4) A
5) C
6) D
7) C

Chapter 9:
1) B
2) C
3) C
4) D
5) A
6) B
7) B

Chapter 10:
1) D
2) A
3) B
4) A
5) B
6) C
7) D

Chapter 11:
1) C
2) B
3) C
4) B
5) D
6) D
7) A

Chapter 12:
1) C
2) B
3) A
4) D
5) C
6) A
7) D

Printed in the USA
CPSIA information can be obtained
at www.ICGtesting.com
LVHW050433280124
769982LV00002B/306

9 781950 321469